B. C. IS
ALIVE
AND WELL

by JOHNNY HART

A FAWCETT GOLD MEDAL BOOK
Fawcett Publications, Inc., Greenwich, Conn.
Member of American Book Publishers Council, Inc.

Other Fawcett Gold Medal Books by Johnny Hart

ZOW

BRUNDT

I HAVE THE ABILITY TO CLOUD MEN'S MINDS SO THAT THEY CANNOT SEE ME.

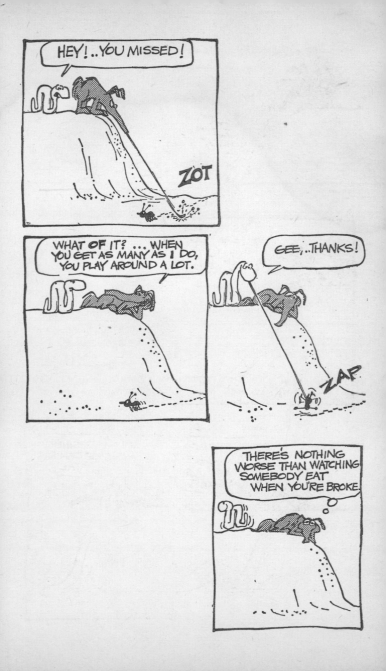

GRONK!

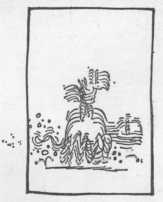

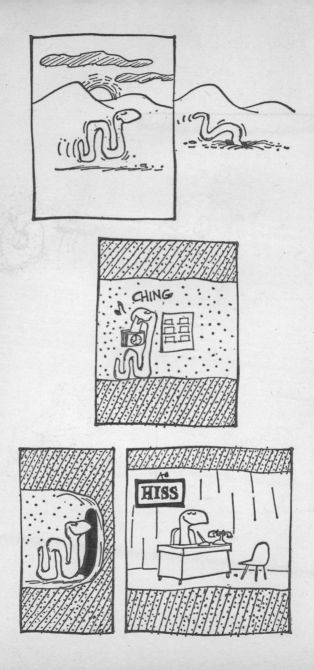

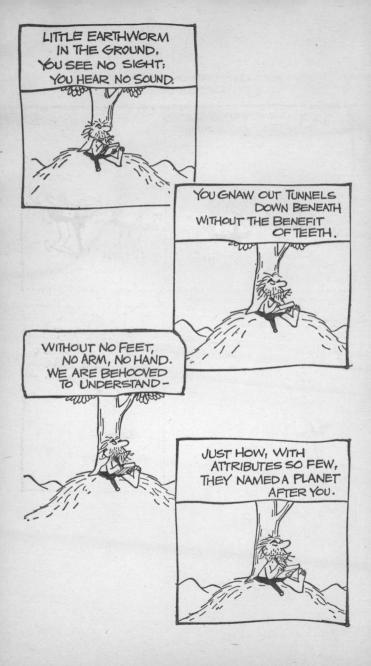

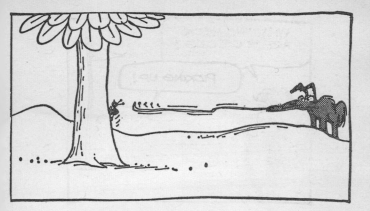

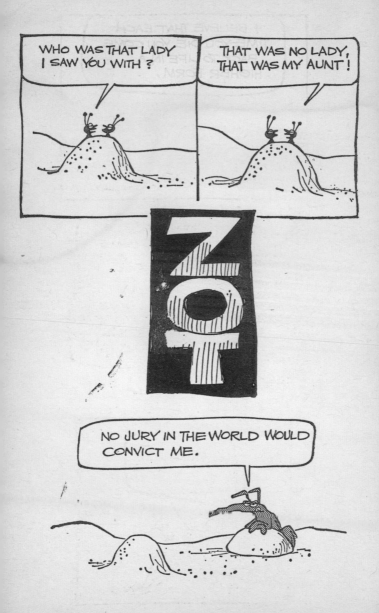

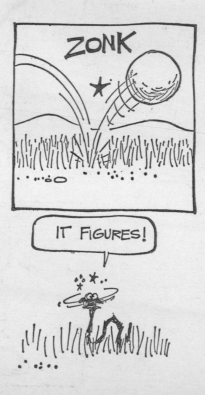

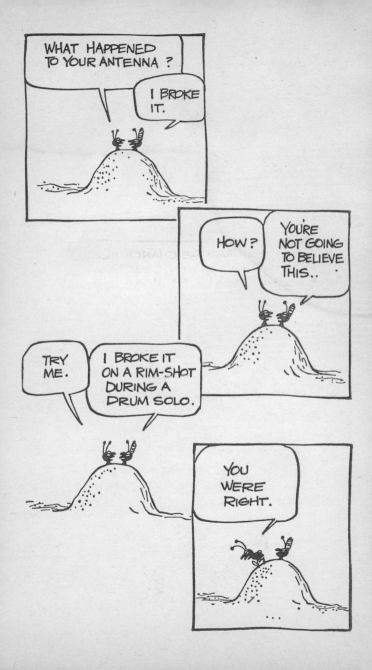

ZIP

SUN
TAN
OIL.

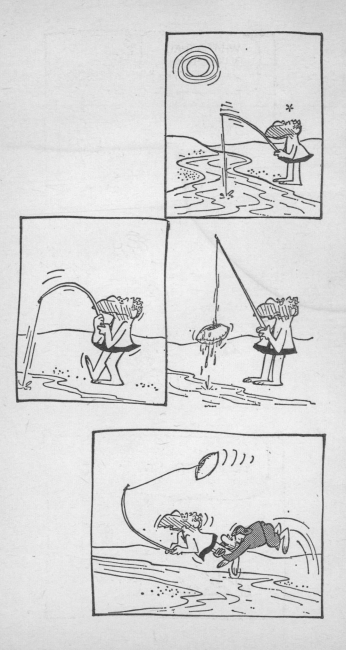